Beyond The Veil Press

TEA WITH MY MONSTER

PROSE

Mental Health Awareness Anthology
Summer 2022

BEYOND THE
VEIL PRESS

CONTENTS

I. Editor's Note   pg. 4

II. Trigger Warning   pg. 5

III. Prose

AJ DeMoyer   *Katabasis and Nepenthe*   *pg. 8*

Diana Hawthorn   *Woman in White*   *pg. 13*

Isabelle Quilty   *The Mountain Grey*   *pg. 16*

Joan Smith Green   *Rule #1*   *pg. 19*

Jonathan Darren Garcia   *Samson*   *pg. 23*

Sarah Eckstine   *you and her #1*   *pg. 26*
                                  you and her #2   *pg. 27*

Syeda Saman Mumtaz Sherazi   *Metamorphosis*   *pg. 30*

Taryn Dorado   *Topographical*   *pg. 33*

Via V. K.   *Pandemic Disco*   *pg. 35*

IV. About The Creators   *pg. 38*

V.   About Beyond The Veil Press   *pg. 39*

VI. Mental Health Resources   *pg. 40*

Editor's Note

Dear Reader,

Like many great things, this project was an accident.

Originally, we planned to include any prose submissions in the first volume of *Tea With My Monster*. Unexpectedly, we got enough submissions that I wanted to give them their own space.

Although they are short stories, this collection does something that poetry can't. It offers more fleshed out characters, plunges you into the middle of their lives, and asks you to sit there with them.

As you read through these slices of lives, I hope it will allow you to look at your own life with a little bit more compassion — through the eyes of a friend instead of your own worst enemy. Each writer weaves their stories in different voices, through a kaleidescope of different lenses. Each writer offers comfort with their own unique gifts. It was healing for me to read these stories over and over throughout the editing process.

When it comes to mental health, we all struggle in different ways, but this collection offers solace in knowing that we are not alone. We are never alone.

Once again, special thanks to **Sophia Mihailidis** for gifting us with the title and **Melia Donk**, whose work appears on the cover.

Lastly, thank you for reading.

Sarah Herrin (she/they)
Beyond The Veil Press

Trigger Warning

Some of these stories may contain mentions of rape, incest, depression, self-harm, and/or suicide.

Please take care of yourself as you read through these experiences and reach out for help if you need it. You are not alone.

US — Suicide Prevention Line: 1.800.273.8255
Sexual Assault Hotline: 1.800.656.4673
Domestic Violence Hotline: 1.800.799.7233
Substance Abuse Hotline: 1.800.662.4357
Self-Harm Textline: Text "Connect" to 741741

UK — Samaritans 116 123

Australia — Lifeline Australia 13 11 14
Beyond Blue 1300 22 4636

More resources at the back of this book and on our website.

Tea With My Monster
Prose

KATABASIS AND NEPENTHE

AJ DeMoyer (@ajdemoyerwriter)

MONDAY

Cleo drags herself into the kitchen for her morning coffee ritual: grind, pour, press. She fills her favourite mug and walks to the backyard. Settles into a creaky chair, its peeling paint wilfully exposing decaying hardwood. Cleo sips the steaming black liquid and, shading her eyes, surveys the garden. Her project. Peter's idea. The doctor was Peter's idea too—she mustn't carry on "like this." *Daughter of Danaus.*

TUESDAY

Cleo wakes to a cockcrow of gunshots and bagpipes. She reaches for her phone. No overnight other-side-of-the-world texts. The ruthless sun beats through the window. Cleo misses frosty mornings and crisp autumn evenings, scarves and mittens, the hard frozen earth.

The nearby military base's live-fire exercises and the private boys' school pipers fall silent. Cleo leaves the bed, pads down the hall. Bathroom. Coffee. She climbs back into bed, careful not to spill her drink. Just a few more minutes. She scratches clusters of pink, swollen mosquito bites on her ankles. Cleo imagines the insects repeatedly penetrating her flesh with their proboscises, injecting their saliva, filling their abdomens with her blood. *Echidna.*

The front door opens, jolting Cleo from her reverie. *Shit!* She jumps out of bed, throws on yesterday's clothes.

"Cleo?" Peter flicks on a light. "Why is the house dark?"

Dark?

WEDNESDAY

Cleo is lucky—her doctor is available Friday at 10am. Would she like that appointment?

Yes.

She practices what to say. "My husband thinks I'm depressed." Cleo pauses. Do I think I am depressed?

She pads into the kitchen. Flicks on the kettle. Finds her favourite mug. Grind. Pour. Press. Checks her phone. No texts, no emails. On social media, a photo of her best friend in LA's crackling fireplace and a selfie of Mimi and Jeff, flush-cheeked in matching ski bibs.

Cleo looks through the kitchen window, notices the plants fading beneath an unforgiving sun. *Helios.*

"I know how you feel," she commiserates.

Peter comes home from work to find Cleo in the garden, lying on her back in the soil, eyes closed, a pair of secateurs in her gloved left hand.

"Cleo?" Peter shakes her shoulder. "What the fuck are you doing?"
"Gardening."
"How long have you been out here?"
"I don't know." She'd been having the most delicious dream—cocooned in an immense cumulus cloud. Silent except for a heartbeat that was not hers; she'd no beating heart. *Morpheus. Epiales.*

THURSDAY

Cleo crumples the note from Peter asking her to buy some toothpaste and deodorant. Please.

She begins her coffee-making ritual and wonders, what would happen if she too had a job? Who would go to the pharmacy for whom? Cleo hadn't not wanted to work.

"Just enjoy life," Peter had said. "I want you to be happy."

Happiness. She walks to the bathroom, looks in the mirror. Her thick hair is separating into greasy bands. *Medusa.* Cleo can't remember when she last washed it. Or herself. She fills the sink with hot water. Grabs a washcloth and a bar of soap. Gives herself a whore's bath. Pits, tits, slits.

Peter smiles. The kitchen counter is littered with onion and garlic skins. The large stock pot bubbles; starchy water splatters against the tiles. Garlicky sauce simmers in another pan.

"Smells delicious."

Cleo's mouth smiles. "It's been a while since I've made dinner."

"It's nice to see you happy." Peter kisses her cheek.

FRIDAY

Cleo sits in a cafe opposite a row of boutiques that line the treeless street. She sips her bitter Americano slowly, waiting to collect her prescription.

"It's understandable," the doctor had observed, "what with your mother's recent death and your significant life changes."

Marriage. Leaving friends and family. Starting over in an unfamiliar, sunburnt country.

Cleo had left the medical centre with a prescription, a psychiatric referral, and the number of a suicide helpline.

Just in case.

SATURDAY

Peter, keen for the first swim of the season, suggests a drive up the coast. Cleo isn't ready for a bathing suit. Her body is soft and lumpy from comfort-eating through the Southern Hemisphere winter, but she doesn't want to disappoint him.

They pack a bag and set off, passing through a string of ticky-tacky neighbourhoods until they pick up the coastal road. The midday sun transforms the ocean into a kaleidoscope of jewels—turquoise, sapphire, emerald. Maybe it would be easier for me here, she reasons, if I could swim. Cleo's chest grows heavy.

That evening, while Peter unpacks the car, Cleo rinses the briny sea from her body. Hot water stings her cheeks, shoulders, chest, belly. Streams down her back, legs, feet. Grains of sand collect on the shower floor. Cleo nudges them towards the drain with her big toe. They catch in the soapy eddy. *Charybdis.* She is grateful to the salty ocean for reddening her eyes; grateful to the shower for washing away her tears.

SUNDAY

Cleo finishes her peanut-butter toast.

"In the morning, on a full stomach to minimise side-effects," her doctor had instructed.

She reaches for the small cardboard box. Turns it over in her hands, inspects the label. Medicine for sorrow. Cleo blinks. Opens the box and slides out a sheet of green and yellow capsules hermetically sealed in individual blisters. Pops a pill through the thin, shiny silver barrier—a featherlight weapon of a Stygian battle. *Euphrosyne and the Algea.*

Cleo takes a sip of water, closes her eyes, and swallows the promise of happiness.

WOMAN IN WHITE
Diana Hawthorn (@diana.hawthorn)

I never meant to hurt anyone.

I ran to the woods to escape my husband.

He had carried me over his threshold on our wedding day, and by our third week of marriage, I knew I would soon be carried out by the undertaker.

I had nowhere to go. As domesticity and I rejected each other, I resigned myself to death in a wild place.

Blood and tears dripped over my lips as I met the forest's edge. I could still hear him shouting behind me. The trees did their best to hide me as I sprinted through their trunks. But there is only so much you can do to hide a white dress on a full moon night.

I came to a steep hillside and ran along the ridge top. His shadow gaining on my every stride.

And then he wasn't.

At the time I thought he had slipped but now I know better.
I couldn't go back to town. They would see the blood on my face and find his broken body in the ravine. What they had politely turned away from in his life, they would burn me for in his death.

I stayed in the woods.

At first, I waited, crouched in a hollow, ears pricking at each twig snap and raven call, sure they would come for me. After a few days, my crouch turned into a slump, slump turned into a defeated slumber.

I lay on damp dead leaves, feeling that I belonged. There was a heaviness inside me that drew me down to the earth.
Winter snows came and wrapped around my body like a blanket. I slept for a season.

As the spring arrived with a sighing thaw, I was roused by the returning birdsong to find a friendly crocus welcoming me back from dreams of dark nights. I smiled upon my reawakening.

I moved in time with the trees, the buds of my heart slowly unfurling as the sunshine kissed my face for the first time in months.

I found I was not hungry, my dress neither damaged nor dirtied. My shoes now pinched my toes and I left them in the hollow.

I wandered over mountains and across lakes. I tended to the forest as though it were my garden. Never taming, no, but mending and singing where I was needed. I sowed the seeds of wildflowers to reclaim fields from slash and plow. We found that we both bore scars of the taking nature of men. We made each other stronger and wilder.

I don't know how long I lived this way before I saw him. My travels had brought me near the trail he traveled. I froze at the sight of him. He spotted me and called out. He thought I needed help.

He moved towards me and the memories of my time spent in the company of men told me to run.

He pursued me to a river. I leapt lightly over the water, whereas he was carried away with the current.

The next man who followed me from a road was torn apart by wolves I had raised from pups.

The next I found three days after he had spotted me, lost in a tangle of buckthorn, succumbed to the cold.

I've lost track of exactly how many men the forest has guarded me against. But it is enough that they have forgotten my name. Now they call me spirit, siren, vengeful woman.

But I never meant to hurt anyone.

Beyond The Veil Press

THE MOUNTAIN GREY
Isabelle Quilty (@thecaffeinebee)

There is a wolf that sits outside my door, he waits and eats all things that aren't allowed inside. I bathe in the glow of isolation, the humorous glints from the ice layering my cabin home. In the fold of the mountains, in the cold eyes of the wastes, I have found a place to work my idle hands. Like my father showed me, I hold and swing the axe with a blunt deftness. The log splits, the fire crackles and in the orange light, I carve memories into pine. Perhaps a little hope surfaces in these moments. Little glimmers of what once was, what could've been. I remember soft little hands, eyes ready to see the wonders of the world and I try to press these small moments into the wood with the serrated metal teeth. But these moments are few, for I know if I wade too deep, I will never surface from those dark waters.

I fill my days with work, my silent wolf by my side. I sort the lumber, hunt, and clear the paths as he keeps watch for the things that haunt the shadows of the mountain. I'm usually of little interest to them. Their tastes lie in the lost travellers, the hikers in the summer that follow their curiosity too far, and the lovers in the springtime seeking a quick thrill in the woods. They find me when they need a healer. Someone that has seen the amalgamations of nightmares, madness, and foul hunger and learnt to live amongst them. I tend to their horns and broken hearts, listening to their troubles in return for oddities and peaceful sleep. Others leave bone carvings and charms, pieces of claws. They decorate the walls of my cabin.

I am a contradiction, in more ways than one. More man than woman, in spite of the womb I carry. Once held on a pedestal, with all the hope of my family's future knotted and stuffed down into my insides. A husband once shadowed me, with thin hands and a nectarine sweet smile. He was pale and splotchy in places with an awkward gait. He wanted a child, and he nearly got it. I held a future in my hands, and let it melt between my fingers.

I cannot bear to live a life half-lived. I will not live in a shield forged at such a tender age that only serves to cage me in, now. How could I justify such a waste? But the snow, the ice, and the darkness are second skin to me. The dawn, snuffed out by clouds and mist older than the woods. A home without a womb, a future warped in reflections seen only in the ice. I live with my hair shaved short, a rifle slung over my shoulder and my brown skin has paled without the warm, honey kisses of the sun shining down.

My father once said, *we are chameleons. In the summer we glow, our melanin loves these riches. In Winter, we might as well stay inside.*

The cabin was his, once. Before a wolf lived by my side, before I gained a second skin, before I was a womb, I stood knee-deep in the snow and watched my father abandon me. The monster that took him appeared like a stag bent backward, to imitate the shape of the full moon. It floated and spoke in a needle-like whisper that strived to dig into my skull. My father took my face into his hands and pressed his forehead against mine. With his rifle slung on his shoulder, he walked into the clearing where the Moon Monster awaited him.

I never saw him again.

Whenever I let my futures turn to salt and run between my fingers, I think of him. He could've turned back, he could've lived.

Now, I will always live as a contradiction. A small, feeble girl too weak to hold a gun cries out for love, to be held. But my skin is ice and my eyes have lost the colour that once wept over violet sunsets and dawns dipped in gold. My wolf walks beside me as he always has, content to eat lesser monsters. His fur is made of shadow, his eyes, too human. Now, he is all the company I need.

The second time the Moon Monster appeared to me, was the last morning I saw the sunrise. A stillness fell over the valley. The snowflakes did not find the ground, the birds each fell silent. I knew this silence, needling and thin as whispers strived to get into my brain.

I followed the whisper to the frozen lake and its deep black beneath the ice.

There, I see you. The body of a doe bent backward, bones splaying from the fur. Frozen beneath the ice, black eyes watching me. Your whispers urge me to join you. It begs, and I hate how my mouth waters at the prospect.

I am salt, earth, and quiet passion, eager for a purpose to be pressed upon me but repugnant at the idea of a concrete future. I am no father, no mother, servant only to the snow and ice. A life half-lived.

The ice cracks.

RULE #1
Joan Smith Green (@joan.s.green)

For me, suicide is mentionable. Mr. Rogers (yes, THE Mr. Rogers of our childhoods) once said, "If it's mentionable, it's manageable." So, let's move forward on that premise into a real-life scenario.

Two people meet. They fall in love and get married. After a while, they decide to start a family. Does this sound familiar? But wait! There is a problem.

What? No pregnancy.

Why? Nearly every friend and family member has a "guaranteed to work" suggestion that runs the gamut of old wives' tales; weekend getaways; drinks; foods; and sexual techniques. Still no pregnancy.

Who? Now the fun begins! See the doctor. Have some tests run. Try this or that simple and easy to follow piece of medical advice. Still no pregnancy. The doctor refers the couple to the best fertility specialist in town. This is serious business. There are more tests; sex on a schedule; charts; pills; procedures; surgeries; powerful, expensive drugs; lots of needles; agonizing waits; tears; fights; and crushing disappointments. It is her fault. He could "repopulate the planet" with that sperm count.

Meanwhile, life keeps going. Family and friends are having babies, beautiful babies and even second and third or more beautiful babies. The couple is happy for their family and friends. They are the best Aunt and Uncle/ Godmother and Godfather/ babysitting team in the world! Every gift they receive says so. Privately, at home together and separately, deep in their hearts the financial, physical, emotional, and mental costs are monumental.

Next? Near the end of one waiting period there is real, strong, nearly confident hope that they truly are pregnant. Her sister calls to say she is unexpectedly pregnant. They talk, laugh, cry, and dream a bit about sharing the experience together. Oh, wouldn't it be special to have children the same year just like Uncle, Mom, and Aunt did in 1966? They hang up; both praying for one more positive pregnancy test the next day.

Morning comes. There is no need to bother with a pregnancy test. He has already gone to work. She cries alone (knowing they will cry together later) as she gets ready and leaves for work.

It rained during the night. The roads are still wet. More rain is expected throughout the day. She is driving down the highway. There are so many emotions and thoughts racing through her mind. Every cell inside her hurts and is screaming in agony! She is so tired of being disappointed and of disappointing him. She just wants the pain to stop; the voice in her head to stop; the questions from others to stop. She wants peace. Where can she find peace?

Looking around for peace, she sees the overpass. That is a thick wall of concrete strong enough to support semis and busses. Surely her little car wouldn't hurt anyone if it hit that overpass. Hmm, is 55 mph fast enough to do the job right? Probably not. How fast is fast enough? 65? 75? 85? 95? 100. She presses the accelerator to the floor. Please, God. Help me do THIS right at least.

The World Health Organization Suicide Data says, "Close to 800,000 people die due to suicide every year, which is one person every 40 seconds. Suicide is a global phenomenon and occurs throughout the life span. [It] is the second leading cause of death among 15-29 year olds globally."

The U.S. Census Bureau data estimates the U.S. Population in 2014 as 318.4 million people. In 2014, the number of suicide deaths is listed as 42,769.

The International Association for Suicide Prevention published the following data on its World Suicide Prevention Day 2019 Facts and Figures Sheet:

> • For every 1 suicide 25 people make a suicide attempt.
> • 135 people is affected by each suicide death.
> • This equates to 108 million people bereaved by suicide worldwide every year.

Data collected 09/18/2020.

I have no clear idea of how I got to work on that day. I remember making the choice to end my life. I remember parking my car and entering my classroom. I only had to pretend to be okay for an hour and a half until the doctor's office opened. I called my regular ob/gyn, not the fertility specialist. His nurse, Marie, said to come on in and tell the folks at the front desk to call her immediately. I was not to sit in the waiting room. I told my principal I had to go to the doctor and left. True to her word, Marie hugged me and took me directly into Ron's office. He had delivered my sister's first child and had spoken with my sister the day before. He had advised her about colleagues he knew in her current city of residence. He held my hand and gave me Kleenex as I told him about the past 24 hours. We agreed I needed a break from trying to get pregnant and that counseling would be an excellent idea.

I learned a few critical truths during the 10-15 years of my infertility journey.

1. Suicide is a permanent solution to a temporary problem.
2. Don't steal your own tomorrow!
3. God has a plan. It is waaaay better than mine!

These truths led me to *RULE #1) God has a plan.* Trust it. Have faith.

Believe it.

How can I be so sure? In 1996 we were blessed with a beautiful baby that we adopted at birth. He was four minutes old when a nurse asked, "Mommy, do you want to meet your son?" On September 18, 2019, his daughter was born. Today, September 18, 2020, his son was born.

Yes, there were struggles before this one. Yes, there have been many struggles since this one. Life is not all sunshine and roses. Sometimes life is hurricanes and shit. Yes, I have had suicidal thoughts since the one described here.

When in doubt refer to *RULE #1) God has a plan.*
God did not let me steal my tomorrow. He had a plan. It beat mine by more than a mile.

Mention how you feel. You are not alone. Reach out for help to manage your despair.

When in doubt, refer to *RULE #1) God has a plan.*

SAMSON'S FIRST WORD

Jonathan Darren Garcia (@Jupiterjazz27)

Samson lies in bed with his eyes open in the dark, watching through his window as the night clouds pass overhead. There is just enough light to write by.

> *Mom is not asleep yet,* Samson writes. *I am lying in bed in the room next to hers. Her snores are so loud I can hear them through the walls.* He pauses, ears straining, but hears nothing yet. *Mom used to never snore. When she gave me this journal, I asked her if she has trouble breathing or if her nose was just made that way. She laughed and said, "Write your jokes here." I don't feel like a joker, but it's a nice journal.*

Everything is quiet but his heart is still beating against his chest.

> *Earlier during the day my mom finally found a little place that can fix and charge dad's old phone. She kept it afterwards all day too. She looked really happy so I was ok with waiting my turn.*

The phone is a little over seven years old. He remembers because the phone is the same age as himself.

> *It was new for dad at the time. My mom said when I was born one of the first things dad did was buy a new phone to record videos and take pictures of us.*

He tries to recollect these moments with his father. He was too young, too little to understand.

> *I don't remember what I was like but mom says I was very happy.*
>
> *When I try to imagine my dad, I try to imagine a bigger me. I can remember glimpses of him but not what he looked or sounded like.*

He reaches into the drawer next to his bed and pulls out a half empty bottle of cologne. The bottle reads "Ever Dream."

> *My only memory of dad is his smell. I can't describe it but I keep his cologne to remember.*

Samson sits up and calms himself. He takes a moment to listen and finally, a raucous snore can be heard through the walls now.

He climbs out of bed and sneaks into his mothers room. Easy enough because she always leaves her door open. Samson picks up his fathers phone from the vanity and runs down the hall and into the kitchen to grab a chocolate chip cookie. Finally, he returns to bed and gets beneath the sheets to hide the light.

After fumbling with the phone a bit he managed to open up the video album. There was only one video and it was titled "Samson's first word."

He pops out of his covers, shuffling to reach for the cologne and spritzes it into the air around him before returning beneath the sheets. He takes a bite out of the cookie and plays the file. The first person he sees is his mom holding a little version of himself.

"Samson— say hi baby!."

He stops chewing. It was the first time he heard his father's voice.

"Say hi baby, say hi to dad." His mother holds his hand and waves it at the camera for him as little Samson is smiling.

"Coco!"

Excitement in his mothers eyes as she turns to look at his dad with an awed smile.

Off camera his father cries, "Babe, what did he say? Samson! What did you say, baby? Babe, hold the phone we have to get this!"

The video spins a jostling scene as his mother takes hold of the phone. The phone's camera takes time to focus. He stares intently searching for a face, his breathing becoming shallow. He forgets all about the cookie and bites the corners of his lips.

It's a big me... A bigger version of himself. It's his dad.

"What did you say my baby, what did you say!?"

"Coco!" Little Samson repeats, smiling, feet wiggling in the air and holding the corners of his fathers smile.

"You want a coco baby? Dad loves you and will give you all the cocos you want!" His father holds him gently with one arm and walks towards the kitchen.

The video ends, and Samson hits play again.

YOU AND HER #1

Sarah Eckstine (@saraheckstine)

i love being with myself

i love existing in this body now after i realized that if no one else is going to love her at least i should

i don't want to give you up again, to anyone, i've realized. am i selfish? or self-preservatory? i don't want anyone else to have you

or am i just scared that if the pain comes again and you're on the inside i'm actually going to be the one to face it

i don't constantly look for people to take care of me anymore, because i know i can do a better job of it than anyone can

it feels like there's a mass of my body, only from the neck down, that exists kinda like a translucent blob of a jelly like material with a lot of air bubbles in it. but she did not exist within me. i took her out, flung her around, pulled at her arms till i thought they would rip from the sockets just to let them go, turn around, and saw the legs off. she was not a part of me, she was a shield for me. but she wasn't my savior. i was her enemy

despite the damage i caused, i didn't let her come to me for recovery, only the fake semblance of restoration before she would be kicked back out

"find someone else"

i expected the same people who broke her to fix her. and when she came to me crying it was a bouquet of the wrong flowers and an empty bed the next morning

i'm sorry for all those years of using you to test the waters but refusing to jump in when you started to drown instead

i'm sorry for all those years i tried to pawn you off to other people, to make you their problem to deal with, and i was the abusive ex you always ran back to for the stability of hurt when nothing was going right. i hope you've forgiven me, or at least are trying

i'd say i won't let anyone hurt her again, but it's because we're together now that i say that. i'm a coward, and could never handle that pain alone

i only let her back in when the pain was gone, i hope she doesn't hate me too much for it

YOU AND HER #2
Sarah Eckstine (@saraheckstine)

it's like i've broken into two people, the "real" me, the soft me, the me that handles the emotions well and is always optimistic is sleeping (or in comatose) in my bed in the fetal position because she can't handle everything that's happening, the same repeated cycle of friends choosing others over you, choosing the people who can drink and smoke and travel easily regardless of how terrible a person they are. the same cycle of my flares, the same cycle of bad luck. she's tired, i don't blame her

what's left however is me, the one writing this, the outer protective shell of her, but without my insides to balance it out, the other, current me, is only left with the suicidal ideation, impulsiveness, depression, mean and manic behavior that the other evens out. i think this is her "payback" in a way, for all the times i forced her to bear everything because i was too much of a coward. she said "your turn" and laid down and went to bed

i don't know when she's going to wake up, but i want to get better so she can have something nice to come home to, so i'm trying to get all my homework done to take the stress off, i'm applying a & d ointment to myself every time i go to the bathroom, i'm preparing for our trip, i don't have an answer to the friend stuff yet, i'll probably need her to help with that, she's always been better at it

i'll be here when you get back.

—

she's awake now but still refuses to get out of bed, we bicker about things we've been through and who's actually been through what, like an old married couple

she keeps peeking her head out from around the corner and seeing the state i'm in and deciding if she wants to come back yet. we usually have a staring contest until she decides to go back to the bedroom

it's no wonder she doesn't want to come back when i'm transcribing the breakup texts between me and our ex boyfriend. there's still a part of me that believes we're going to get back together, and i know that exists in her too so she's going to ignore me even harder

—

she's come out to the couch with me now, we're sitting on opposite ends with our knees up and kicking each other every once in a while to try and take up more space. i'm reading a story about someone taking care of their partner's chronic pain

that's where we're the same, that's something we both want and can agree on, maybe that's why she's getting closer again, because we both realize that we're the only person we have that takes care of us

—

we decided to tackle the friendship situation together, and we've been back together since, but i'm still in the main caretaker. she's content to reside within my chest rather than out of me for now, at least

METAMORPHOSIS
Syeda Saman Mumtaz Sherazi

Metamorphosis. I kept making doodles around the word absentmindedly while taking it in. In biological term, its just the change in the physical structure or form that takes the body to its final stage of transformation, but in psychology it's the change that's happening on the inside that most people are unaware of, but that is what really makes us "Us".

It can either result in us adjusting like everyone or take us to our extinction depending upon our very first connection or relationship, our parents. The change starts from there and then and through all the stages till the final, the connections around us are for the most part involved in shaping our personality. Our siblings, friends, teachers and our spouse after parents.

I kept looking at the word I wrote on my notebook and then my gaze searched and stopped on someone who could be the perfect example for this term.

I have seen him change from an insecure and shy primary schooler to a ghost of a human being with hollow eyes that were uninterested and unfazed by his surroundings in middle school and now here he's switching between the troublemaker to being invisible.

When we are little and nearly unconscious of everything happening with and around us, it's where it started, living with a suicidal mother and a bipolar father. They made him what he is today, disassociated and an outcast with mental instability issues but nobody is going to blame the parents and to them he's just a messed up case because they haven't really seen him, seen the "real" him. They have seen the side of him that he wants to show and these people are actually dumb enough to actually believe him or it's much easier for them to do so since it's seems less complicated.

He keeps flickering between wind and a storm and I think I understand him, he wants to be the wind to protect himself where all he needs is to be invisible and nobody could know about him or his feelings, its like having no existence, but that's what scares him. Being the wind does helps us in keeping us from our fears for a while but then it makes us worry about not existing, we have to prove to ourselves more then anyone else that we are being seen and that we do exist so that's where the wind becomes the storm and it makes sure that everyone is aware of this being. This is why he keeps switching between the two, to keep in contact with this wilderness by maintaining a safe distance so to be far enough from their reach. So getting detentions, locking himself somewhere nobody could find him and all those things that a troublemaker does were what he was known for.

Lately, I can see him taking pleasure in being the wind so he wouldn't have his energy wasted, and watching him fade away makes me feel guilty but I know better that I can't help him, not because I don't want to but because he won't take it. He doesn't like it. He never liked it. Nothing can heal the shattered mind, like no one can put the pieces of broken glass back together, not even love. The damage is already done. The stages where he should have developed trust and his identity, all he went through was mistrust, shame, doubt, inferiority and role confusion.

His ego(it keeps the Id and superego in balance) lost in the balancing game of his superego (that works to discipline us according to morality principles) and his Id (that works in satisfying our own desires) that ended up getting caught in a conflict internally and he lost himself in the war of his mind. According to Sigmund Freud, when this happens, then destruction is inevitable — that's when one thinks of suicide and no one else can help if he doesn't want it. Even when his eyes scream for help — when he looks this way, his words are always the same:

"leave me alone" or "go away".

TOPOGRAPHICAL
Taryn Dorado (@tdorado21)

They say that when you learn something new or create a new memory, your brain forms a new wrinkle… forever altering it's appearance, marking that moment permanently. I think about these peaks and valleys that make up my brain. Are they all the same? Do happy memories look like smooth cascading bits of grey matter dipping deep into the brain… wanting to make sure that they will never be forgotten?

What about painful memories? Do they form chaotic fractured crevices, ripping and tearing my brain matter, scaring it, proving to the happy memories that they will indeed be the ones that are long remembered? The ones that will be felt the deepest. The ones that will last.

I don't know if the brain actually does this. Could it really start out as a smooth mound of tissue? When I die, what will my brain look like? Will it resemble a battle field torn apart with thick scars being the only thing that held it together. Or will the expansive folds of happiness be more prominent… smoothing the pain, covering it in the joys that life gave me?

Sometimes I wish I could crack open my skull and take a peek. To be comforted on my darkest days that indeed I've had more velvety valleys than jagged rocky fractures. To know that this life is worth living, that I'm made up of more joy than pain… more happiness than sorrow.

PANDEMIC DISCO
VIA V. K. (@cinderconecrucible)

The first month was a vicious beast. Having been subjected to the forced contemplation of December, I was in no rush to relive the agony of my existential crisis, and yet I quickly found myself in the jaws of jarring January. It is that time of the year when the winter's gone and the air is still, nothing ever moves. The first week was unbearable. Nothing like watching vicious, drunk accidents and saying, *Happy new year!* at the same time.

February made for a strange bedfellow. Have you ever scrutinised yourself in the third person, watching your life ebb in eddies, the flow weaker and weaker? A most painful dilution, such were my days. The whole thing though, it was painless, and that was shocking because going through a life change wasn't supposed to feel like that. I fear I was forced into a goodbye I was not ready for, my cocoon was cut open and I was writhing on the floor with my sticky, mottled wings. People, like life usually does, went on. It is easier for my fellows to accept life as it is, I applaud them. Truly, adulthood cannot allow for distractions, and to be rendered meek by something as fickle as time?

And yet march into the third month, and et voilà! I was smack dab in the middle of a global health crisis. WHO was updating its website, guidelines were written (and then re-written), masks and sanitisers costed triple (if you could find them), the social medicine department finally got its day in the sun, and I was sitting in a rural health clinic with no PPE and a receptionist who coughed a little too much for comfort. And what did I do this entire time? I binge-watched a criminal profiling show on Netflix (you get points if you guess which one). I had mounting academic commitments and a pressing concern - my own safety, and somehow my mobile phone and a set of earphones did more for me than WHO ever could (meaning no disrespect). Coffee - clinic - snacks - repeat. The coffee cup got bigger each day, it was cheap and it felt good and that was sorely lacking by mid-March. Have you experienced the Indian summer heat in a tropical place while forced to sit in a little room wearing your lab coat, with cobwebs for friends? You won't look so puzzled, then. I cut my hair very short and looked a bit like Willy Wonka, but there are no golden tickets in this story.

Months April and May don't exist, of course. I drove to June, punch drunk in a motorcycle without a helmet on and with my eyes closed. June seemed a lovely lady; she introduced me to my first few likes on Instagram, and I was back like an addict in withdrawal very soon. They don't exactly pat your back and smile at you; when you work in a hospital, everybody hates you. The nurses hate you and make you fill out all these forms because they don't have the authority; the patients hate you because, well, cirrhotic patients mustn't drink, diabetic patients must make lifestyle changes, and stroke patients don't recover as quickly as we'd all like. Then your superiors, they hate you on principle because 'you're stupid'. Six people liked me on June the seventeenth which is more than all the people in my entire class in all of 2019, and if you think I'd exaggerate in matters like these, then you don't know me at all.

Some time in mid-2020, it occurred to me: I could write poetry. Not that anyone cared, but it was like magic. I could wave my wand and words arranged themselves. And I wasn't even doing anything. I wrote obsessively from July to November. I was first published during the pandemic. The pandemic! Ah, I had almost forgotten or rather, I had denied its existence for months. Instead, I would log in to take tests that I knew I'd perform poorly because 'it's just rigged that way to prepare you for the big day', then I'd eat processed food that I'd strictly advise my patients against, skip meals and wear the same clothes twice in a row. The possibility of being confronted by reality dangled over my head like a sword, so I walked the line like a monkey in a circus, and life would throw coins at me. However, the rush of the numbers game faded fast, and I was back to plugging the hole in the dam with my thumb.

In the month before the last one for the year, I stood in front of a mirror and asked myself what I wanted. If I wanted to make something of myself, I had to see the bigger picture and work backwards. But the face in the mirror smiled awkwardly and looked away, so I went back to responding to e-mails because it's the polite thing to do. I interviewed a celebrity, did you know? I'll imagine you clapping for me because I do enjoy a good display of validation.

I have eagerly bowed to masters I don't serve, laughed harder than I intended to, fought battles without outcomes, and learned the same lessons one too many times; these don't add up, but I don't think anyone noticed.

If you ask me, the mask reveals more than it hides. Look at their eyes, do they avert their gaze? Do they crinkle at the corners? Do they widen? Do they moisten? Here's my verdict because I think this ramble has gone on too long:

The pandemic is to civilians what a penitentiary is to criminals. No, I don't mean that it is a prison. It is, in a way, a liberation. A showing of the true self, a magician's 'flourish of the hands' reveal. I have seen man's true nature, worthy of an episode in Black Mirror. For the first time, I have seen society's underbelly. God slammed his gavel and man was condemned to twelve fatal lashes.

Technology killed humanity, internet is the new reality. But what about me?

Well, what about me, indeed?

ABOUT THE CREATORS

AJ DeMoyer (she/her) is a writer living in New South Wales, Australia. She is studying an MA (Writing & Literature) with Deakin University; researching gender and socio-political ideologies in dystopian fiction. When not writing or reading, she likes to bake, hike the local rainforest, and tend her cactus garden. *IG: @ajdemoyerwriter*

Diana Hawthorn (she/her) is a Canadian writer. She writes poetry and short stories centered on ecofeminism, family histories, and the various shapes of love. She is a historian and a museum professional. In her spare time, she hikes with her dogs. *IG: @diana.hawthorn*

Isabelle Quilty (they/them) is a non-binary writer from regional Australia. They have been published with *ENID Network, #Enbylife, Demure, Kindling and Sage, Queer as Fiction,* and an upcoming anthology set to be published mid-2022. *IG: @thecaffeinebee*

Joan Smith Green (she/her) is a widow, mom, Jamma, sister, friend, and retired educator. She has survived rape; defeated alcoholism; earned a black belt in Kempo Karate; become disabled while working; loved and lost. *IG: @joan.s.green*

Jonathan Darren Garcia (he/him) is a San Antonio based writer that has been featured in many literary magazines including *That Gray Zine, Crepe and Penn, From Whisper to Roars, Royal Rose,* and *Scum Gentry Arts*. He enjoys the simple things: a good cup of coffee, hiking, and a good book. *IG: @Jupiterjazz27*

Sarah Eckstine (she/her) is a photographer and writer based in Normal, Illinois. She completed a BFA in Photography at the Maryland Institute College of Art and is an MFA student at Illinois State University. Her work focuses on her life as a woman with chronic health issues and borderline personality disorder. *IG: @saraheckstine*

Syeda Saman Mumtaz Sherazi (she/her) is a Pakistani Fine Arts student. She enjoys writing about psychology, spirituality, and astrology.

Taryn Dorado (she/her) is a writer, an educator, and dog mom. Born in Southern California, she now resides on the other sunny coast. She loves hiking in nature or happily failing at her new hobby: surfing. You can find her with her nose stuck in a book or editing her first novel. IG: *@tdorado21*

Via V. K. (she/her) is a freelance writer in their twenties. She is a doctor residing in India. Her work has been published in platforms like the *Train River Anthologies* and *the Whippoorwill Quarterly Press*. She is drawn to themes that are greater than man, nature, mystery, macabre, and fantasy, while also enjoying the gift of the everyday life. *IG: @cinderconecrucible*

ABOUT BEYOND THE VEIL PRESS

Beyond The Veil Press is an indie publisher of poetry & art, based in Colorado, and founded by two art school graduates in Spring 2021. We are strong advocates of Mental Health Awareness and donate a percentage of each book sale to a featured mental health nonprofit. True to our name, we love all things spooky, blurring boundaries, and shedding light on the mysterious unknown.

Whether you need support yourself or hope to support a loved one, we encourage you to visit the Mental Health Resources page on our website.

Beyond The Veil Press is run by poet/artist/survivor **Sarah Herrin** (she/they), with the support of poet **AJ Wojtalik** (she/her).

Web: *beyondtheveilpress.com*
IG: *@beyondtheveilpress*
FB: */beyondtheveilpress*

MENTAL HEALTH RESOURCES

BOOKS

The Body Keeps The Score – Bessel van der Kolk
The Journey From Abandonment To Healing – Susan Anderson
Waking The Tiger - Peter Levine
Polysecure: Attachment, Trauma, & Consensual Nonmonogamy – Jessica Fern

WEBSITES

Active Minds - Mental health awareness and education for students. *activeminds.org*

American Foundation for Suicide Prevention - Saving lives and bringing hope to those affected by suicide. *afsp.org*

Anxiety & Depression Society of America - Prevention, treatment, and cure of anxiety, depression, OCD, PTSD, and co-occurring disorders through education, practice, and research. *adaa.org*

The Psych Collective - actionable resources and real skills to help people make meaningful change in managing mental health issues. *thepsychcollective.com*

The Trevor Project - Crisis intervention and suicide prevention services to lesbian, gay, bisexual, transgender, queer, and questioning youth. *thetrevorproject.org*

National Institute of Mental Health - Research on mental disorders. *nimh.nih.gov*

PODCASTS

Being Well - Rick Hanson, Forrest Hanson
Where Is My Mind? – Niall Breslin
The Savvy Psychologist: Quick & Dirty Tips – Jade Wu
The Hilarious World of Depression – John Moe
The Happiness Lab – Dr. Laurie Santos

APPS

Headspace: Meditation and Sleep Made Simple

More resources available on our website.